EASIEST
KEYBOARD
COLLECTION

The Corrs

WISE PUBLICATIONS
London/New York/Paris/Sydney/Copenhagen/Madrid

Exclusive Distributors:

Music Sales Limited
8/9 Frith Street,
London W1V 5TZ, England.

Music Sales Pty Limited
120 Rothschild Avenue,
Rosebery, NSW 2018,
Australia.

Order No. AM959849
ISBN 0-7119-7794-1
This book © Copyright 1999 by Wise Publications

Cover design by Chloë Alexander
Compiled by Peter Evans
Music arranged by Roger Day
Music processed by Paul Ewers Music Design

Printed in the United Kingdom by
Caligraving Limited, Thetford, Norfolk.

Cover photograph courtesy of London Features International

Your Guarantee of Quality
As publishers, we strive to produce every book to the highest
commercial standards.
The music has been freshly engraved and the book has been carefully
designed to minimise awkward page turns and to make playing from
it a real pleasure.
Particular care has been given to specifying acid-free, neutral-sized
paper made from pulps which have not been elemental chlorine
bleached. This pulp is from farmed sustainable forests and was
produced with special regard for the environment.
Throughout, the printing and binding have been planned to ensure
a sturdy, attractive publication which should give years of enjoyment.
If your copy fails to meet our high standards, please inform us and
we will gladly replace it.

Music Sales' complete catalogue describes thousands of titles and is
available in full colour sections by subject, direct from Music Sales
Limited. Please state your areas of interest and send a cheque/postal
order for £1.50 for postage to: Music Sales Limited, Newmarket Road,
Bury St. Edmunds, Suffolk IP33 3YB.

www.musicsales.co.uk

Contents

CLOSER

Words & Music by Andrea Corr, Caroline Corr, Sharon Corr & Jim Corr

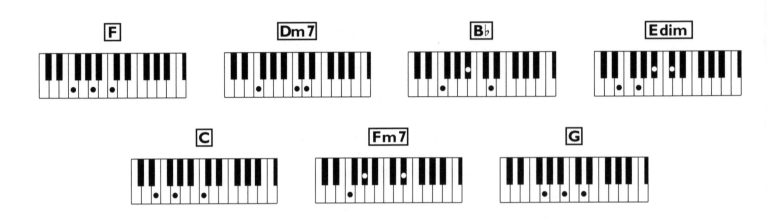

Voice: **Flute**
Rhythm: **Love Ballad**
Tempo: ♩. = 52

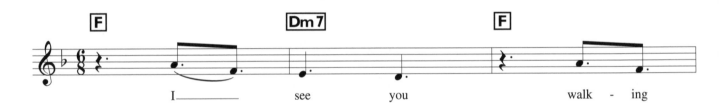

I_____ see you walk - ing

ev - 'ry - day_____ with a smile be - neath the frown._____

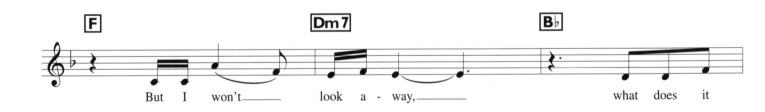

But I won't_____ look a - way,_____ what does it

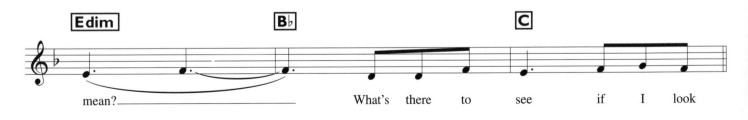

mean?_____ What's there to see if I look

DON'T SAY YOU LOVE ME

Words & Music by Andrea Corr, Caroline Corr, Sharon Corr, Jim Corr & Carole Bayer Sager

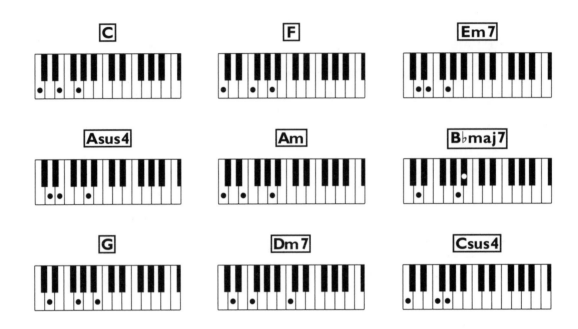

Voice: **Electric Piano 2**

Rhythm: **Pop Ballad**

Tempo: ♩ = 76

I've seen this place a thou - sand times,___ I've

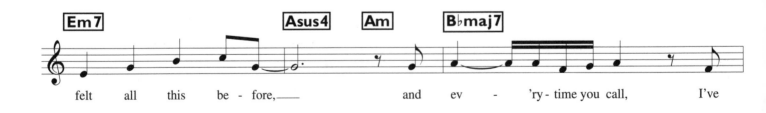

felt all this be - fore,___ and ev - 'ry - time you call, I've

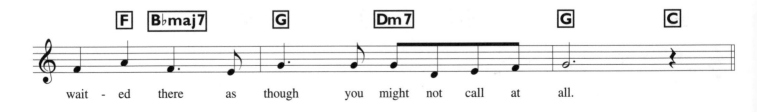

wait - ed there as though you might not call at all.

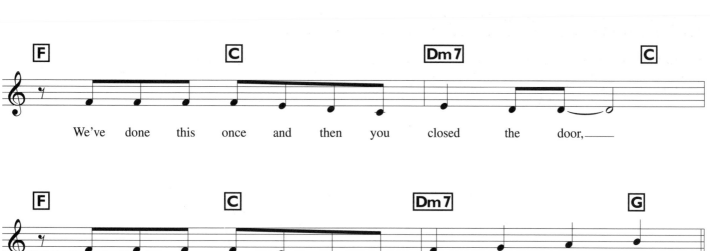

We've done this once and then you closed the door,_____

don't let me fall a - gain for no - thing more. Don't

say you love me un - less for - ev - er. Don't

tell me you need me if you're not gon - na stay. Don't

give me this feel - ing, I'll on - ly be - lieve it.

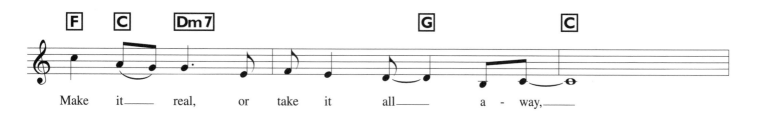

Make it_____ real, or take it all_____ a - way,_____

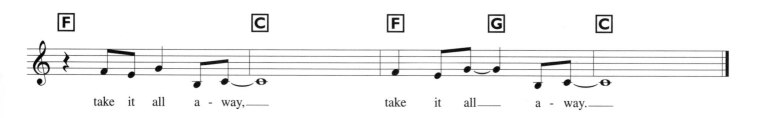

take it all a - way,_____ take it all_____ a - way._____

DREAMS

Words & Music by Stevie Nicks
© Copyright 1977 Welsh Witch Music, USA.
Sony/ATV Music Publishing (UK) Limited, 10 Great Marlborough Street, London W1.
All Rights Reserved. International Copyright Secured.

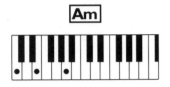 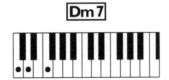 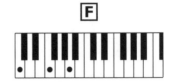 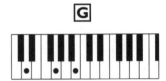

Voice: **Acoustic Guitar**

Rhythm: **Lite Pop**

Tempo: ♩ = 128

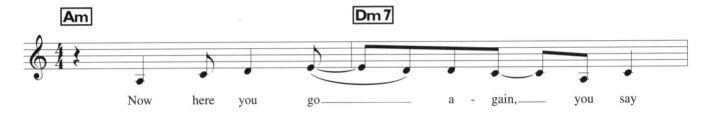

Now here you go———— a - gain,—— you say

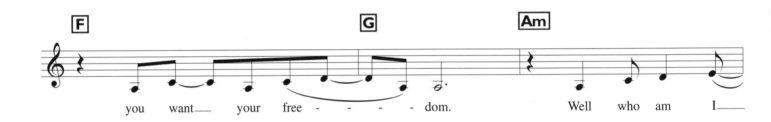

you want—— your free - - - - dom. Well who am I——

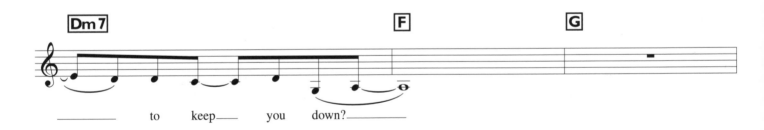

———— to keep—— you down?——

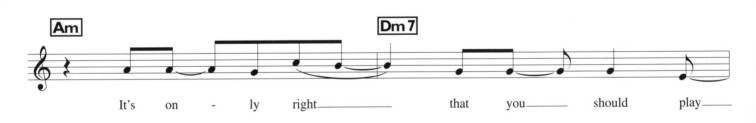

It's on - ly right—————— that you—— should play——

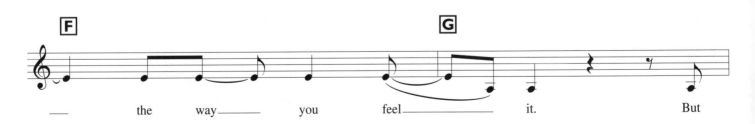

—— the way—— you feel———— it. But

FORGIVEN, NOT FORGOTTEN

Words & Music by Andrea Corr, Caroline Corr, Sharon Corr & Jim Corr

HEAVEN KNOWS

Words & Music by Andrea Corr, Caroline Corr, Sharon Corr & Jim Corr

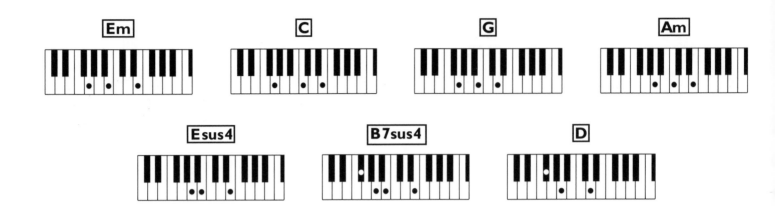

Voice: **Acoustc Guitar**

Rhythm: **Soul Ballad**

Tempo: ♩ = 100

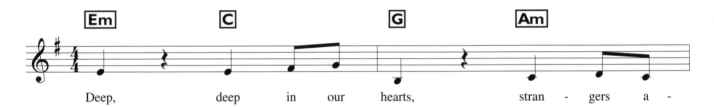

Deep, deep in our hearts, stran - gers a -

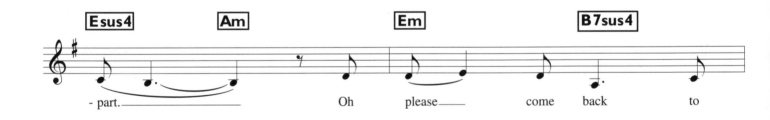

- part._____ Oh please____ come back to

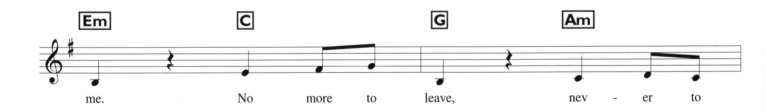

me. No more to leave, nev - er to

grieve,_____ I give my world to

HOPELESSLY ADDICTED

Words & Music by Andrea Corr, Caroline Corr, Sharon Corr, Jim Corr & Oliver Leiber

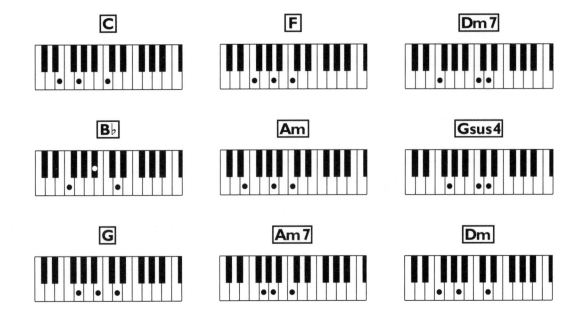

Voice: **Flute**

Rhythm: **Folky Pop**

Tempo: ♩ = 92

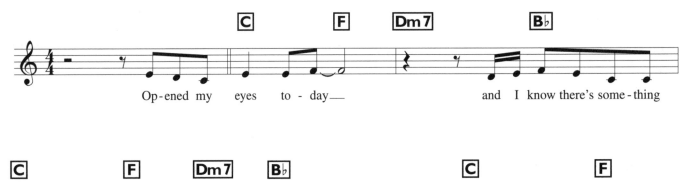

Op-ened my eyes to-day___ and I know there's some-thing

diff-'rent. I saw you in a brand new way,___

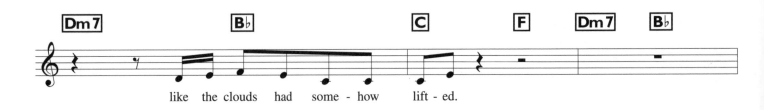

like the clouds had some-how lift-ed.

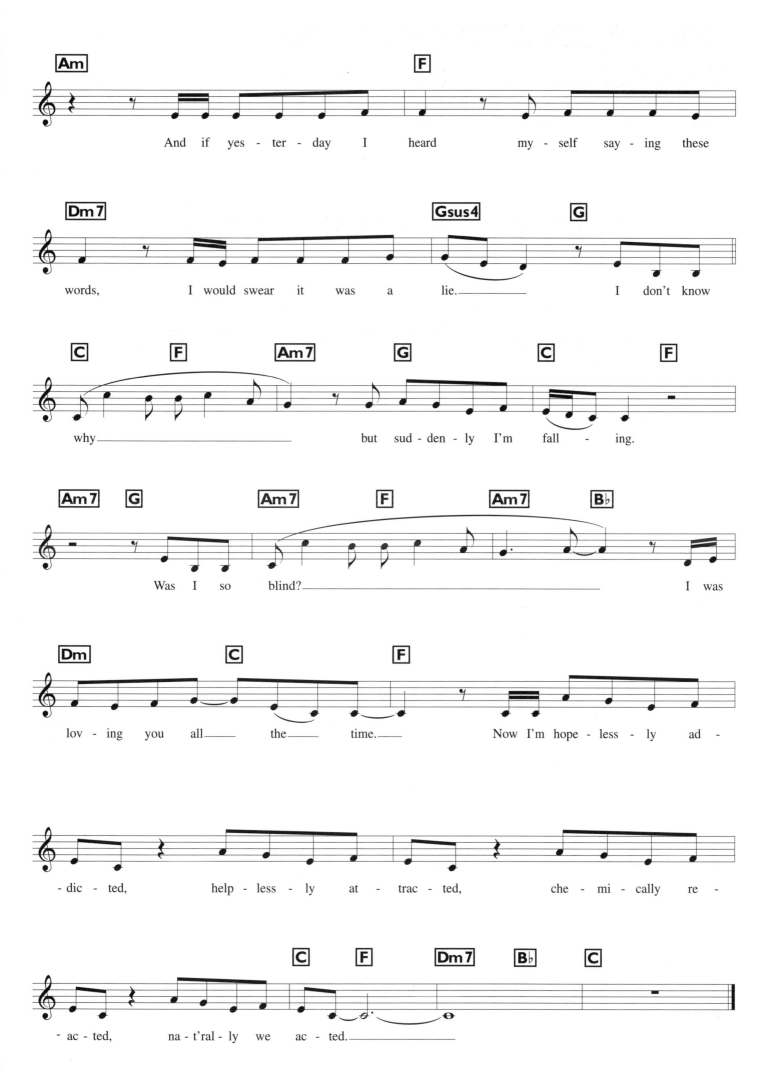

I NEVER LOVED YOU ANYWAY

Words & Music by Andrea Corr, Caroline Corr, Sharon Corr, Jim Corr & Carole Bayer Sager
© *Copyright 1997 Beacon Communications Music Corporation/Songs of PolyGram International Incorporated & All About Me Music, USA.*
PolyGram Music Publishing Limited, 47 British Grove, London W4 (66.67%) &
Warner Chappell Music Limited, Griffin House, 161 Hammersmith Road, London W6 (33.33%).
All Rights Reserved. International Copyright Secured.

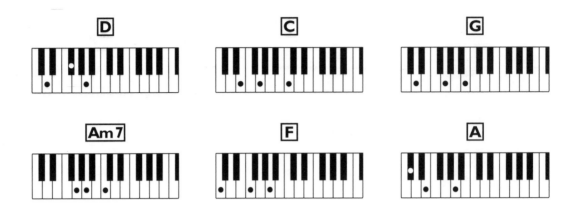

Voice: **Clarinet**

Rhythm: **Soft Rock 1**

Tempo: ♩ = 102

You bored—— me with your sto - ries,

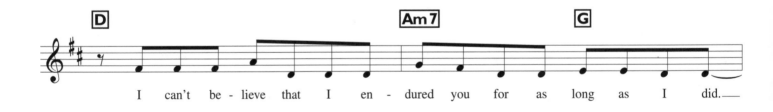

I can't be - lieve that I en - dured you for as long as I did.——

—— I'm hap - - py it's o - - ver,

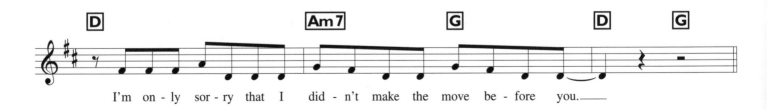

I'm on - ly sor - ry that I did - n't make the move be - fore you.——

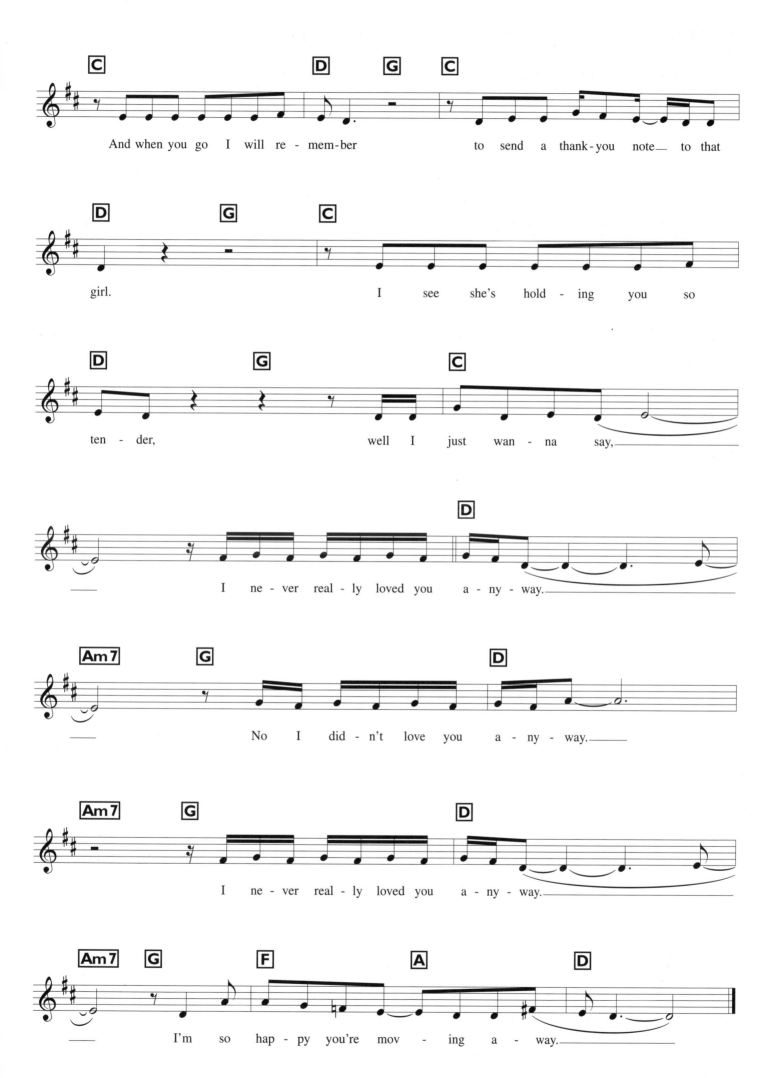

INTIMACY

Words & Music by Billy Steinberg, Rick Nowels & Neil Giraldo

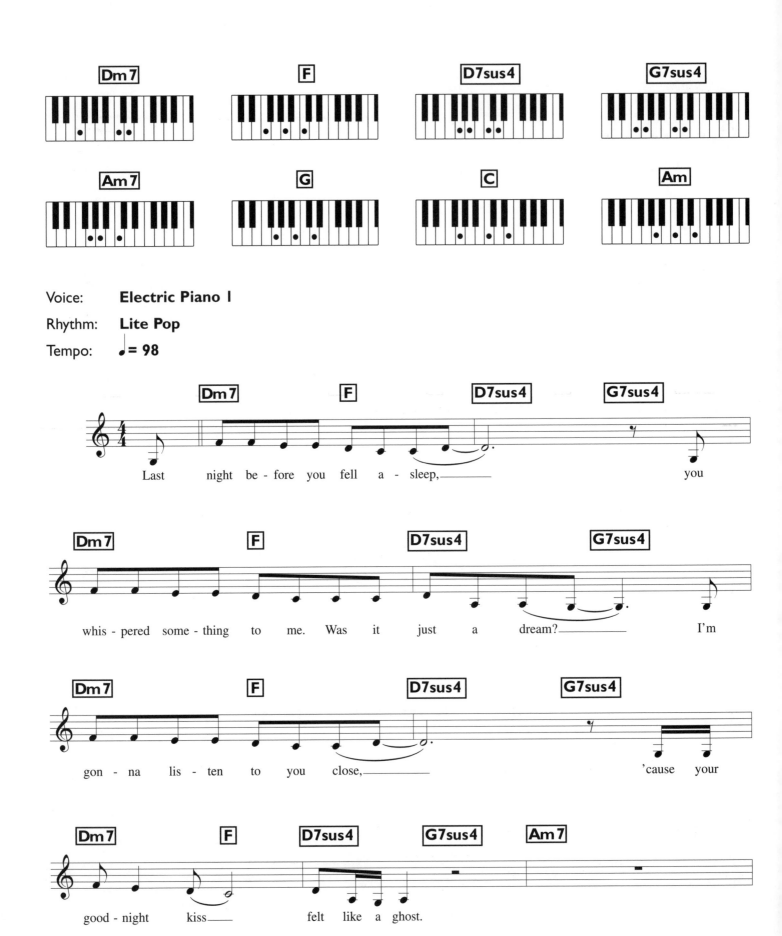

Voice: **Electric Piano 1**

Rhythm: **Lite Pop**

Tempo: ♩ = 98

Last night be-fore you fell a-sleep,_____ you

whis-pered some-thing to me. Was it just a dream?_____ I'm

gon-na lis-ten to you close,_____ 'cause your

good-night kiss_____ felt like a ghost.

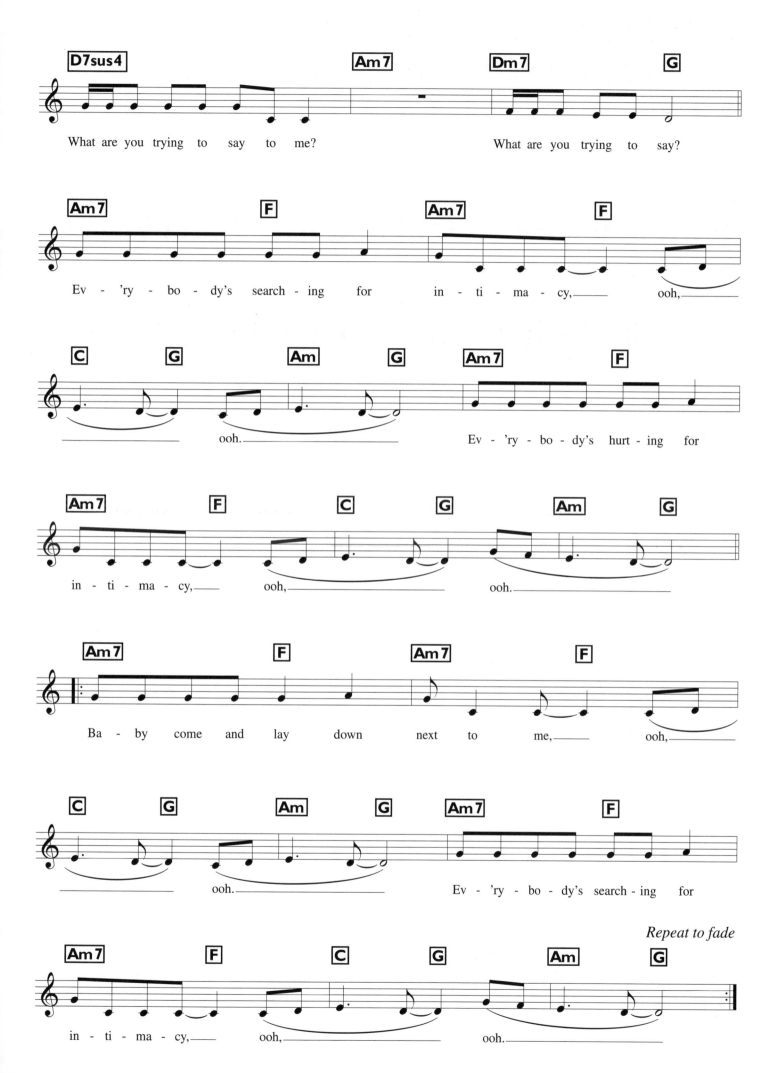

LEAVE ME ALONE

Words & Music by Andrea Corr, Caroline Corr, Sharon Corr & Jim Corr

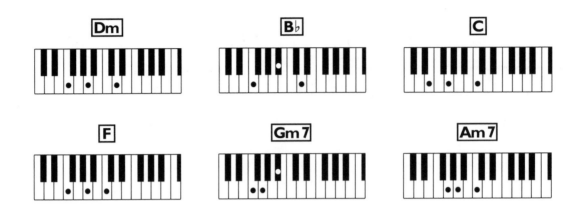

Voice: **Piano**

Rhythm: **Folky Pop**

Tempo: ♩ = 120

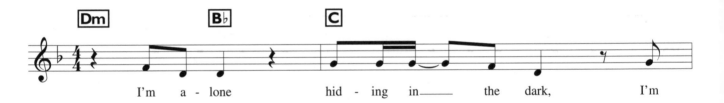

I'm a - lone hid - ing in___ the dark, I'm

look - ing for a life to come and res - cue me.

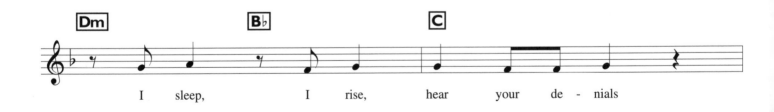

I sleep, I rise, hear your de - nials

end - less - ly in - side. It's cra - zy but

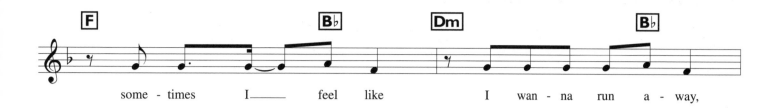

some - times I____ feel like I wan - na run a - way,

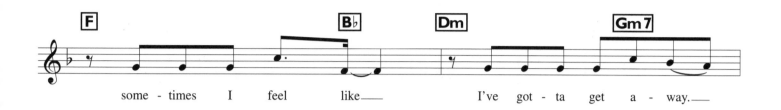

some - times I feel like____ I've got - ta get a - way.____

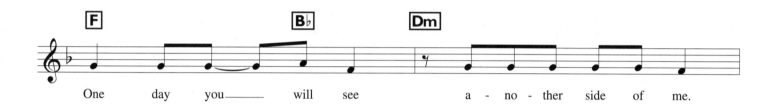

One day you____ will see a - no - ther side of me.

My life I____ com - mand, it's not the way that you planned.

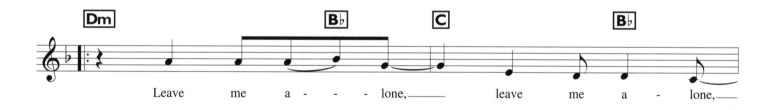

Leave me a - - - lone,____ leave me a - lone,____

Repeat to fade

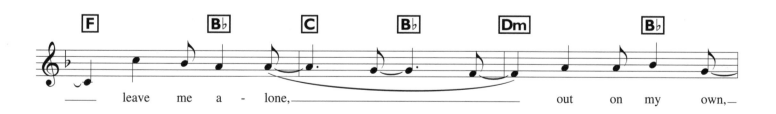

____ leave me a - lone,_____ out on my own,____

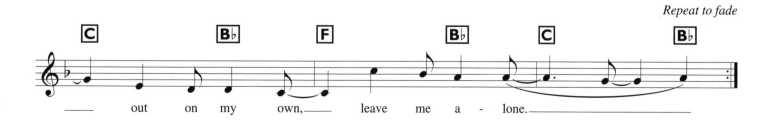

____ out on my own,____ leave me a - lone.____

LOVE GIVES LOVE TAKES

Words & Music by Andrea Corr, Sean Hosein, Dane De Viller, Stacey Piersa, Elliot Wolff & Oliver Leiber

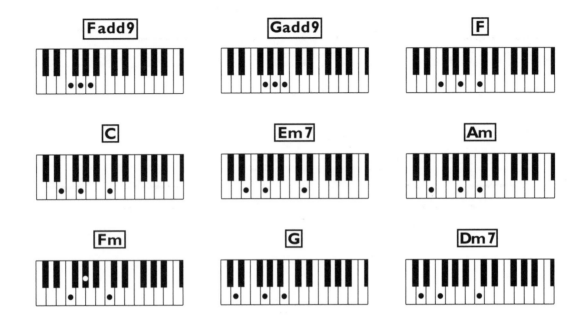

Voice: **Choir**

Rhythm: **Soft Rock 1**

Tempo: ♩ = 98

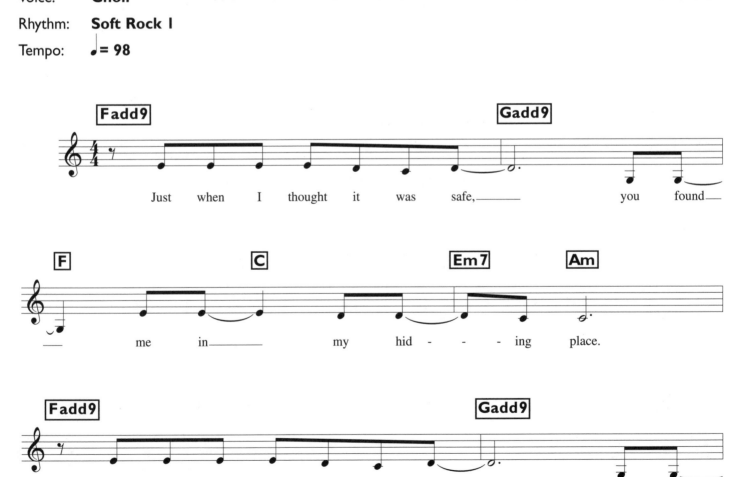

Just when I thought it was safe,_____ you found_____ me in_____ my hid - - - ing place.

I'd pro - mised ne - ver a - gain,_____ I would -

LOVE TO LOVE YOU

Words & Music by Andrea Corr, Caroline Corr, Sharon Corr & Jim Corr

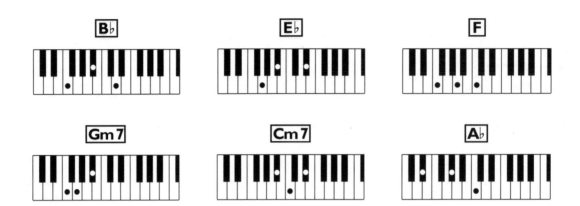

Voice: **Alto Saxophone**

Rhythm: **Dance Pop 1**

Tempo: ♩ = 84

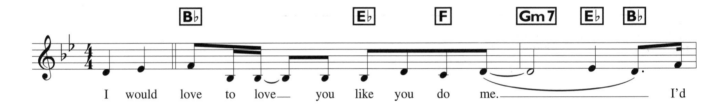

I would love to love— you like you do me.————— I'd

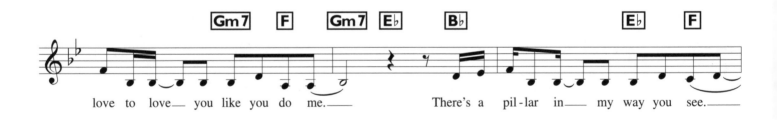

love to love— you like you do me.— There's a pil-lar in— my way you see.—

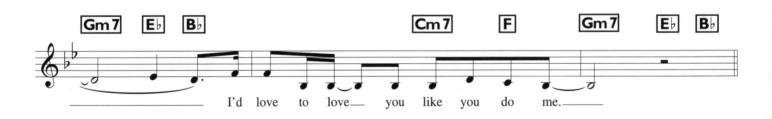

I'd love to love— you like you do me.—

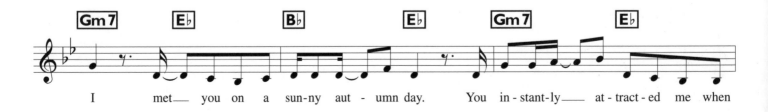

I met— you on a sun-ny aut-umn day. You in-stant-ly— at-tract-ed me when

ask - ing for— the way. God, if I had known the pain I'd make— you feel, I would have stopped- this thought of us and turned u - pon— my heel.— Though you— should leave me, time make— it be all right. Though you— must leave me, be - lieve me when— I tell you I would love to love— you like you do me.———————— I'd love to love— you like you do me.— There's a pil - lar in— my way you see.———————— I'd love to love— you like you do me.——— Break— those pil - lars

Repeat to fade

(down.—) Break— those pil - lars down.

NO GOOD FOR ME

Words & Music by Andrea Corr, Caroline Corr, Sharon Corr & Jim Corr

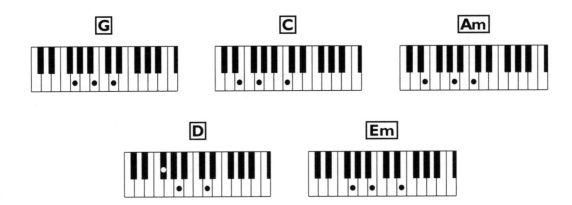

Voice: **12 String Guitar**

Rhythm: **Country**

Tempo: ♩ = 92

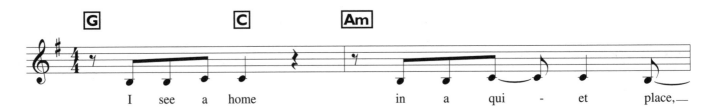

I see a home in a qui-et place,

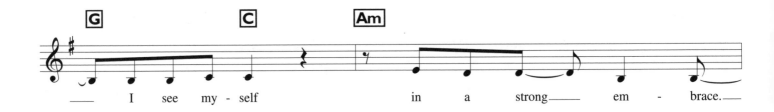

I see my-self in a strong em-brace.

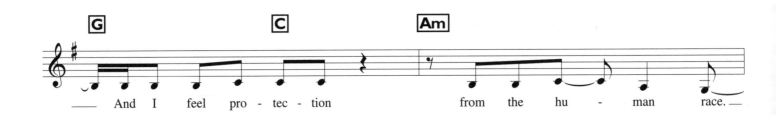

And I feel pro-tec-tion from the hu-man race.

It's not pa-ren-tal, but it's a fan-ta-sy,

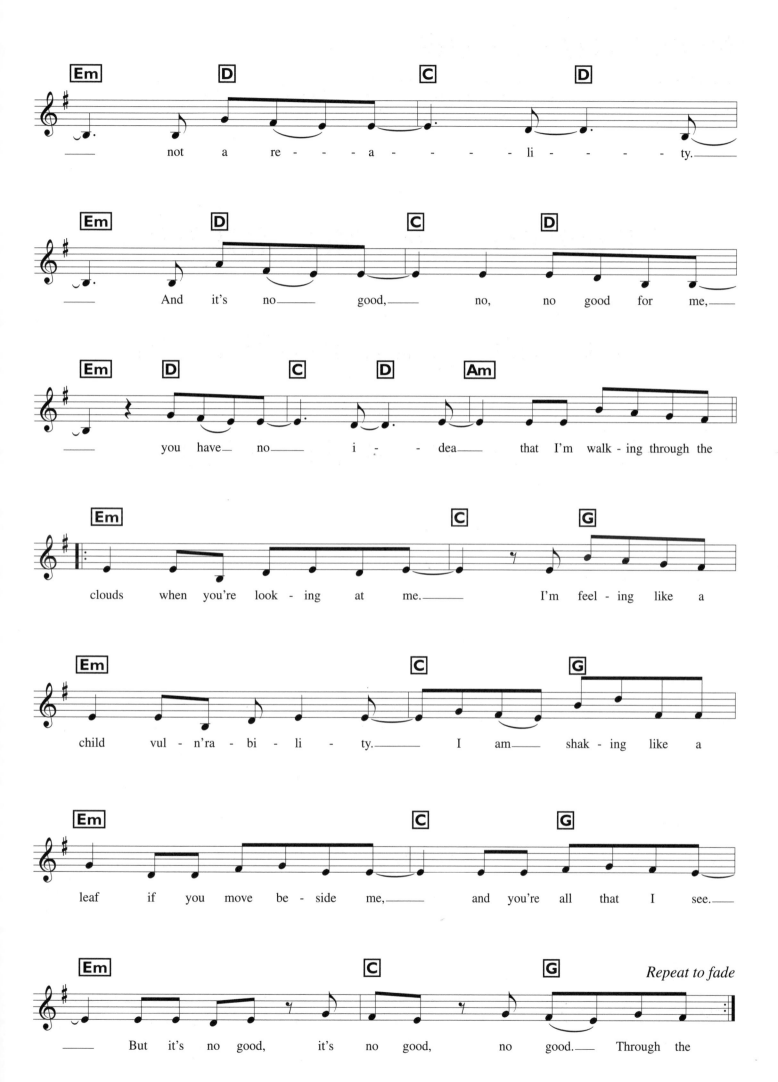

ONLY WHEN I SLEEP

Words & Music by Andrea Corr, Caroline Corr, Sharon Corr, Jim Corr, John Shanks, Paul Peterson & Oliver Leiber

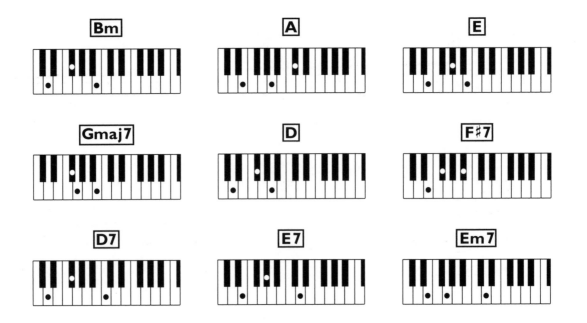

Voice: **Distortion Guitar**

Rhythm: **Pop Fusion**

Tempo: ♩ = 76

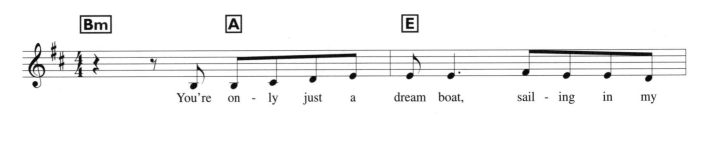

You're on-ly just a dream boat, sail-ing in my

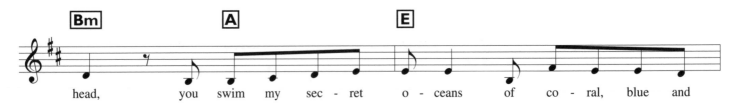

head, you swim my sec-ret o-ceans of co-ral, blue and

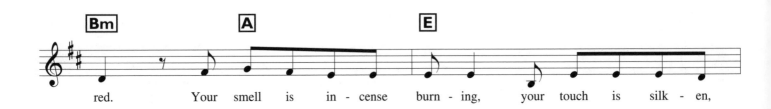

red. Your smell is in-cense burn-ing, your touch is silk-en,

yet it reach - es through my skin, mov - ing from with -

- in, and clutch - es at my breast. But it's on - ly when I

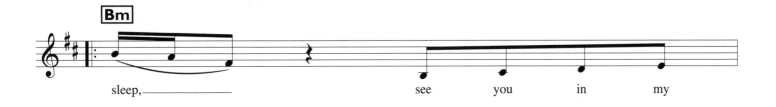

sleep,_____ see you in my

dreams, got me spin - ning round and round,___ turn - ing

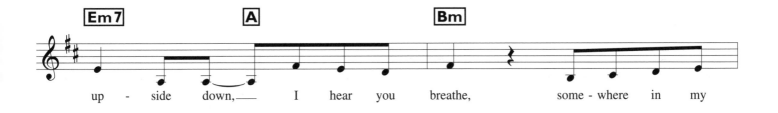

up - side down,___ I hear you breathe, some - where in my

sleep, got me spin - ning round and round,___ turn - ing

Repeat to fade

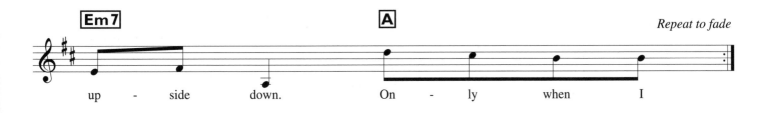

up - side down. On - ly when I

QUEEN OF HOLLYWOOD

Words & Music by Andrea Corr, Caroline Corr, Sharon Corr, Jim Corr, Glen Ballard, Dane De Viller & Sean Hosein

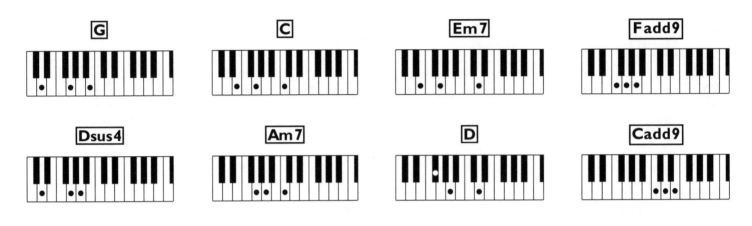

Voice: **Violin**

Rhythm: **Acoustic Guitar**

Tempo: ♩= **94**

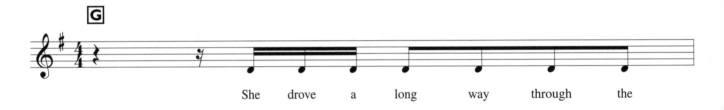

She drove a long way through the

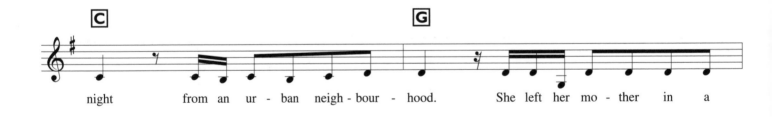

night from an ur-ban neigh-bour-hood. She left her mo-ther in a

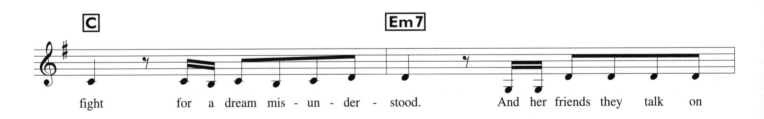

fight for a dream mis-un-der-stood. And her friends they talk on

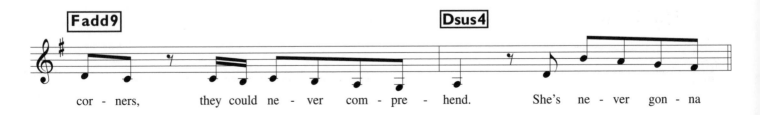

cor-ners, they could ne-ver com-pre-hend. She's ne-ver gon-na

be   like   the   one   be -   fore,_____   she   read   it   in   her

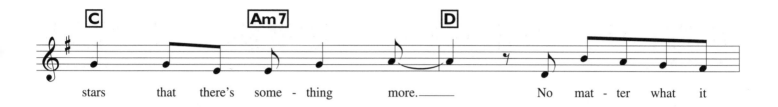

stars   that   there's   some -   thing   more._____   No   mat -   ter   what   it

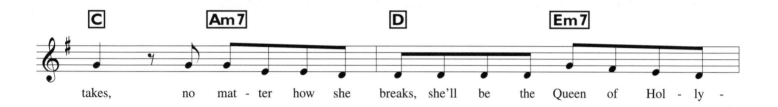

takes,   no   mat -   ter   how   she   breaks,   she'll   be   the   Queen   of   Hol - ly -

- wood.   She   is   the   Queen   of   Hol - ly -

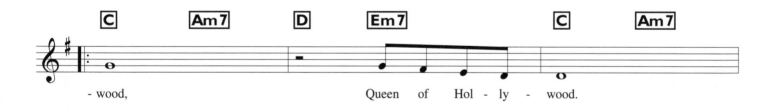

- wood,   Queen   of   Hol - ly - wood.

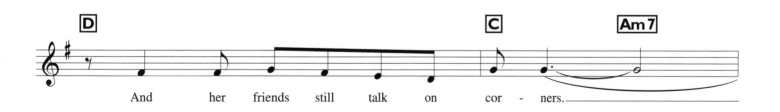

And   her   friends   still   talk   on   cor -   ners._____

Repeat to fade

She   is   the   Queen   of   Hol - ly -

RUNAWAY

Words & Music by Andrea Corr, Caroline Corr, Sharon Corr & Jim Corr
© Copyright 1995 Beacon Communications Music Corporation/Songs of PolyGram International Incorporated, USA.
PolyGram Music Publishing Limited, 47 British Grove, London W4.
All Rights Reserved. International Copyright Secured.

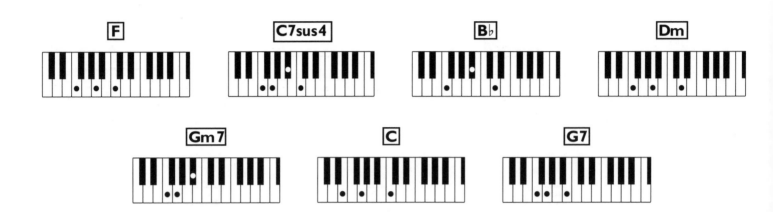

Voice: **Flute**

Rhythm: **Love Ballad**

Tempo: ♩. = **52**

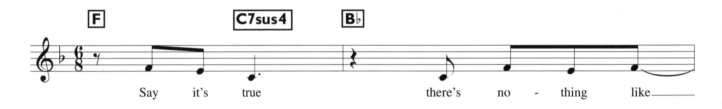

Say it's true there's no - thing like me and you.

—— me and you. I'm just a - lone,

tell me you—— feel it too. And I would

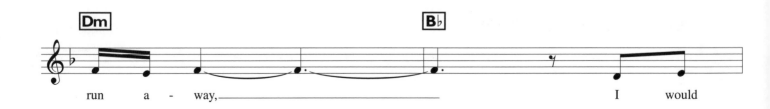

run a - way,———————— I would

SECRET LIFE

Words & Music by Andrea Corr, Caroline Corr, Sharon Corr & Jim Corr

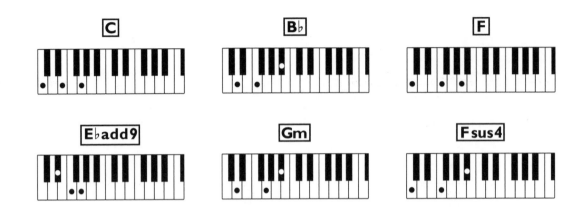

Voice: **Clarinet**

Rhythm: **Funky Pop 1**

Tempo: ♩ = 96

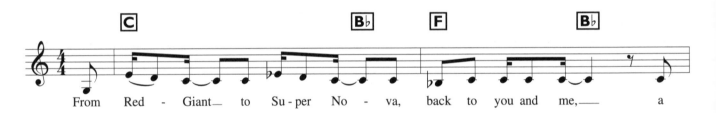

From Red - Giant to Su - per No - va, back to you and me,____ a

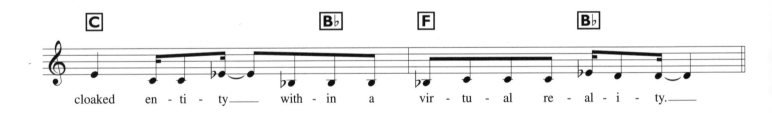

cloaked en - ti - ty____ with - in a vir - tu - al re - al - i - ty.____

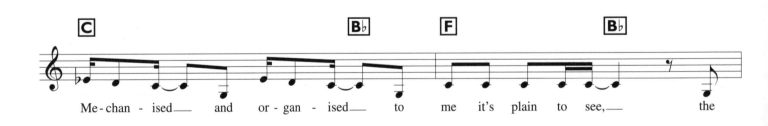

Me - chan - ised____ and or - gan - ised____ to me it's plain to see,____ the

hand that's been bu - sy weav - ing fan - ta - sy,____ it's so

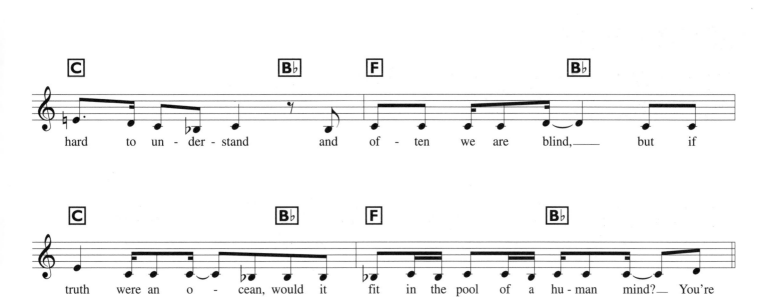

C **B♭** **F** **B♭**

hard to un - der - stand and of - ten we are blind,____ but if

C **B♭** **F** **B♭**

truth were an o - cean, would it fit in the pool of a hu - man mind?___ You're

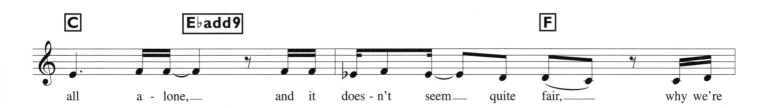

C **E♭add9** **F**

all a - lone,___ and it does - n't seem___ quite fair,___ why we're

C **E♭add9** **F** **C** **E♭add9**

all left in ig - no - rance,___ turn-ing to___ de - spair,___ phi - lo - so - phy___ and the - o - lo - gy___

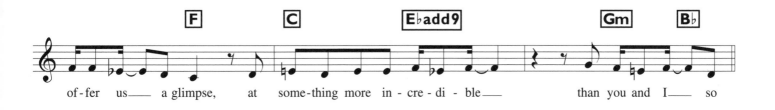

F **C** **E♭add9** **Gm** **B♭**

of - fer us___ a glimpse, at some-thing more in - cre - di - ble___ than you and I___ so

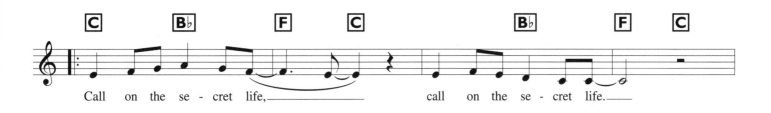

C **B♭** **F** **C** **B♭** **F** **C**

Call on the se - cret life,_____ call on the se - cret life.___

Repeat to fade

B♭ **F** **C** **B♭** **Fsus4** **F** **C**

Show me the way of life,_____ bring on the se - cret life.___

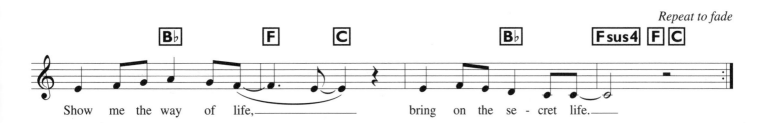

SO YOUNG

Words & Music by Andrea Corr, Caroline Corr, Sharon Corr & Jim Corr

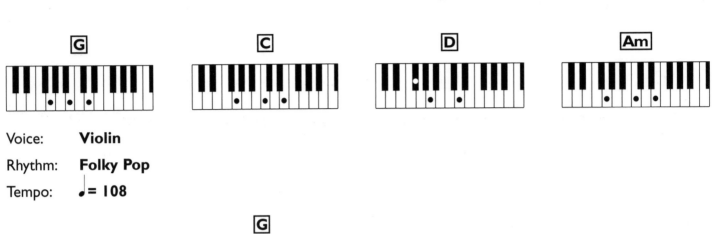

Voice: **Violin**

Rhythm: **Folky Pop**

Tempo: ♩ = 108

We were tak - ing it ea - - - sy,

bright and bree - - zy,____ yeah.____

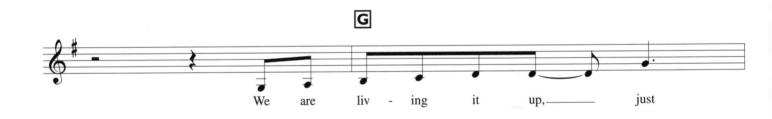

We are liv - ing it up,____ just

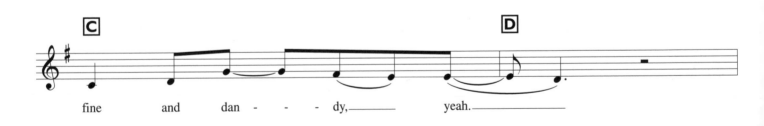

fine and dan - - dy,____ yeah.____

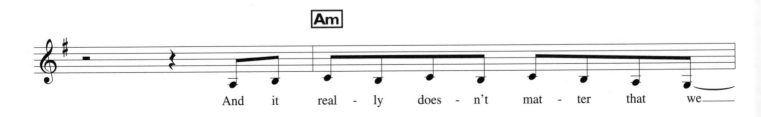

And it real - ly does - n't mat - ter that we____

SOMEDAY

Words & Music by Andrea Corr, Caroline Corr, Sharon Corr, Jim Corr & David Foster

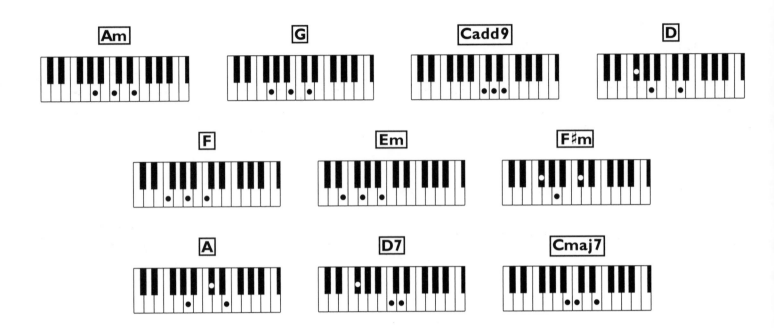

Voice: **Choir**

Rhythm: **Pop Ballad**

Tempo: ♩ = 100

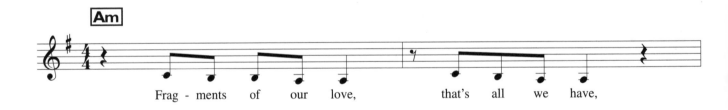

Frag - ments of our love, that's all we have,

what we had was fan - ta - sy, dreams___ and pho - to - graphs.

Hyp - no - tic me - lo - dies could sing our song, a com - for - ta - ble rhy - thm in a

THE MINSTREL BOY

Traditional
Arranged by Andrea Corr, Caroline Corr, Sharon Corr & Jim Corr
© Copyright 1995 Beacon Communications Music Corporation/Songs Of PolyGram International Incorporated, USA.
PolyGram Music Publishing Limited, 47 British Grove, London W4.
All Rights Reserved. International Copyright Secured.

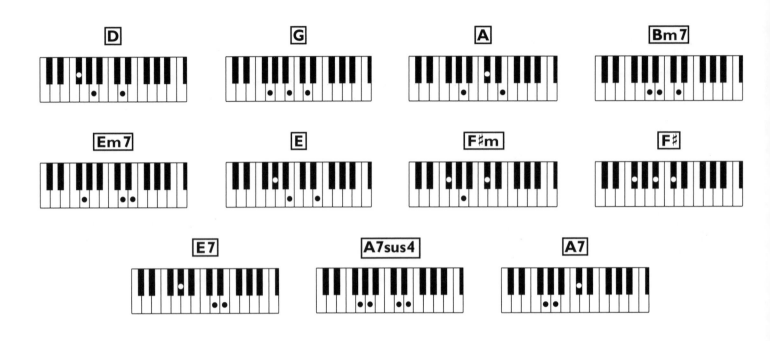

Voice:　**Violin**

Rhythm:　**Folk**

Tempo:　♩ = 72

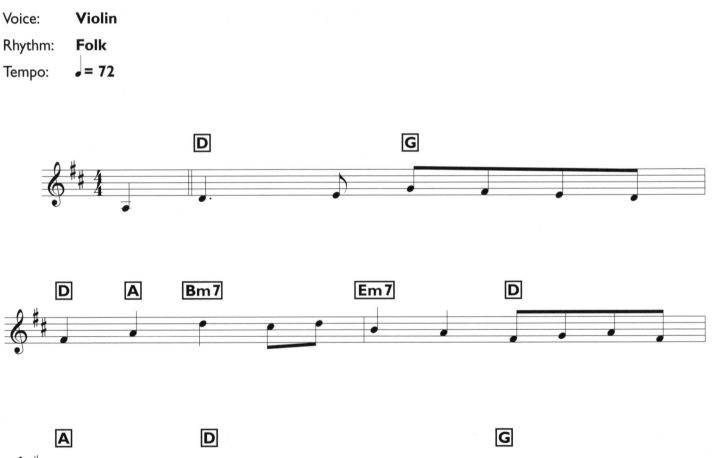

THE RIGHT TIME

Words & Music by Andrea Corr, Caroline Corr, Sharon Corr & Jim Corr

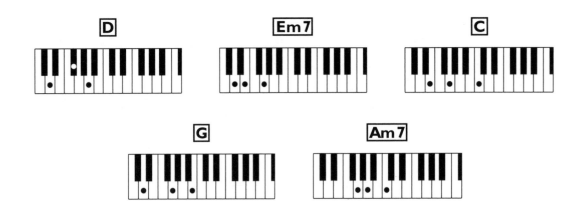

Voice: **Studio Piano**

Rhythm: **8 Beat Shuffle**

Tempo: ♩ = 96

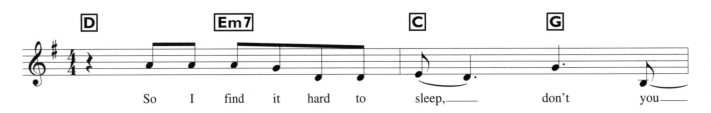

So I find it hard to sleep,____ don't you____

____ know.____ The sun is shin-ing in my

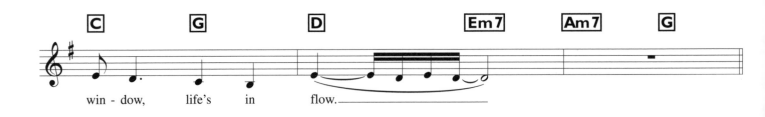

win-dow, life's in flow._____

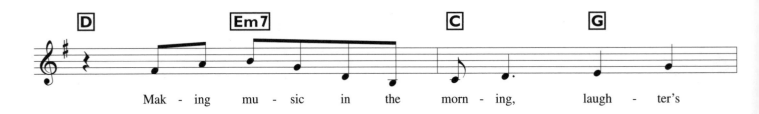

Mak-ing mu-sic in the morn-ing, laugh-ter's

WHAT CAN I DO

Words & Music by Andrea Corr, Caroline Corr, Sharon Corr & Jim Corr

 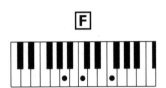  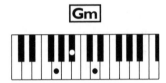

Voice: **Alto Saxophone**

Rhythm: **Folksy Pop**

Tempo: ♩ = 80

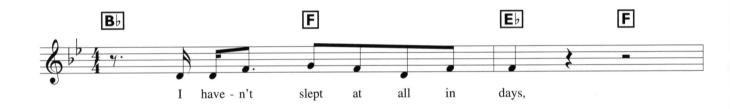

I have-n't slept at all in days,

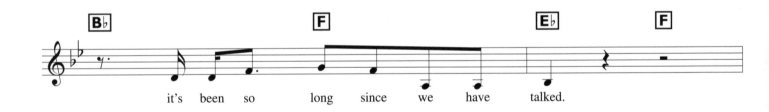

it's been so long since we have talked.

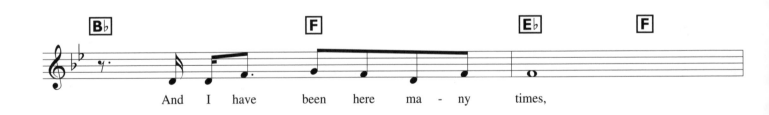

And I have been here ma-ny times,

I just don't know what I'm do-in' wrong.

What can I do—— to make you care?—— What can I say—— to make you

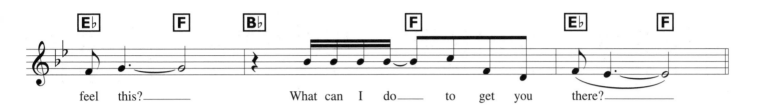

feel this?—— What can I do—— to get you there?——

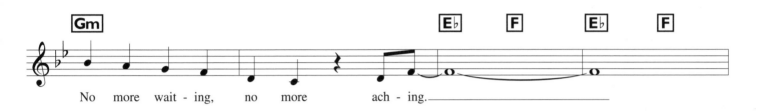

No more wait - ing, no more ach - ing.——

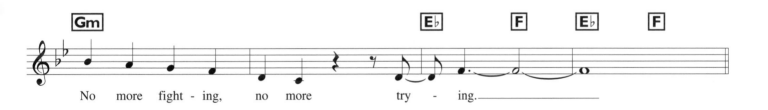

No more fight - ing, no more try - ing.——

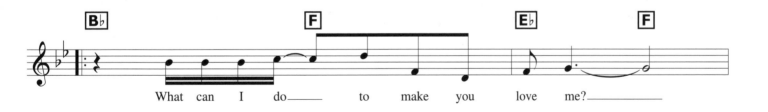

What can I do—— to make you love me?——

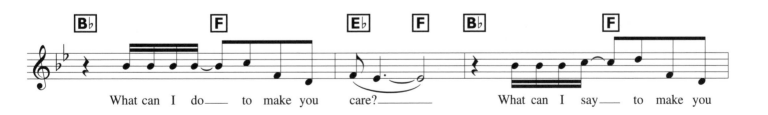

What can I do—— to make you care?—— What can I say—— to make you

Repeat to fade

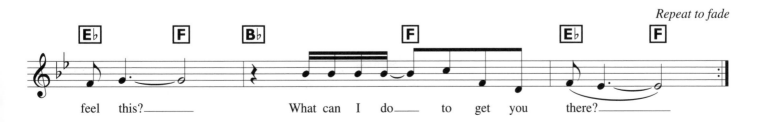

feel this?—— What can I do—— to get you there?——

WHEN HE'S NOT AROUND

Words & Music by Andrea Corr, Caroline Corr, Sharon Corr & Jim Corr
© Copyright 1997 Beacon Communications Music Corporation/Songs of PolyGram International Incorporated, USA.
PolyGram Music Publishing Limited, 47 British Grove, London W4.
All Rights Reserved. International Copyright Secured.

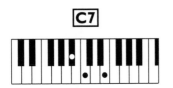
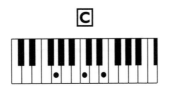
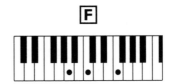
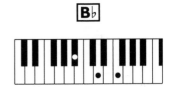

Voice: **Distortion Guitar**

Rhythm: **New Age**

Tempo: ♩ = 88

He's un - - cool, an un - so -

- phi - sti - cat. He's a tight - rope walk - er on an

op - en path. He's a maze of cu - ri -

- o - si - ty. He is the liv - ing___ bread___ that cures my

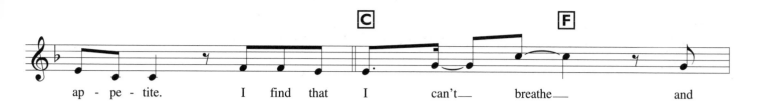

ap - pe - tite. I find that I can't breathe   and

I can't sleep   when he's not a - round.

     Ev - 'ry - - day   is

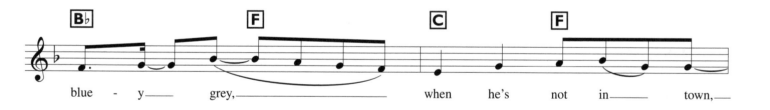

blue - y grey,   when he's not in town,

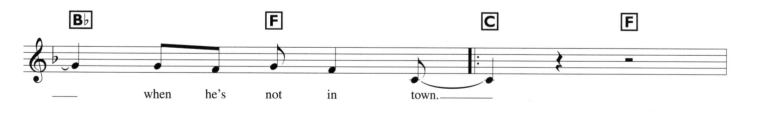

 when he's not in town.

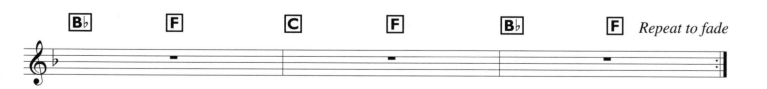

Repeat to fade

EASIEST KEYBOARD COLLECTION

Easy-to-play melody line arrangements for all keyboards with chord symbols and lyrics. Suggested registration, rhythm and tempo are included for each song together with keyboard diagrams showing left-hand chord voicings used.

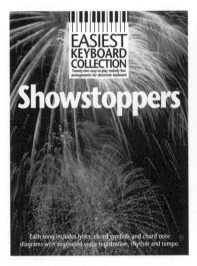
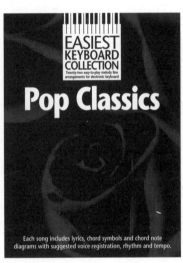
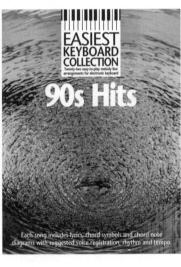

Showstoppers
Consider Yourself (Oliver!), Do You Hear The People Sing? (Les Misérables), I Know Him So Well (Chess), Maria (West Side Story), Smoke Gets In Your Eyes (Roberta) and 17 more big stage hits.
Order No. AM944218

Pop Classics
A Whiter Shade Of Pale (Procol Harum), Bridge Over Troubled Water (Simon & Garfunkel), Crocodile Rock (Elton John) and nineteen more classic pop hits, including Hey Jude (The Beatles), Imagine (John Lennon), Massachusetts (The Bee Gees) and Stars (Simply Red).
Order No. AM944196

90s Hits
Over twenty of the greatest hits of the 1990s, including Always (Bon Jovi), Fields Of Gold (Sting), Have I Told You Lately (Rod Stewart), One Sweet Day (Mariah Carey), Say You'll Be There (Spice Girls), and Wonderwall (Oasis).
Order No. AM944229

TV Themes
Twenty-two great themes from popular TV series, including Casualty, EastEnders, Gladiators, Heartbeat, I'm Always Here (Baywatch), Red Dwarf and The Black Adder.
Order No. AM944207

Also available...

Ballads, Order No. AM952116   **Film Themes**, Order No. AM952050
Boyzone, Order No. AM958331   **Hits of the 90s**, Order No. AM955780
Broadway, Order No. AM952127   **Jazz Classics**, Order No. AM952061
Chart Hits, Order No. AM952083   **Love Songs**, Order No. AM950708
Christmas, Order No. AM952105   **Pop Hits**, Order No. AM952072
Classic Blues, Order No. AM950697   **60s Hits**, Order No. AM955768
Classical Themes, Order No. AM952094   **80s Hits**, Order No. AM955779